Daisy Lane Home–School Reader

Toy trouble

by Carol Matchett

Schofield & Sims

It's toy time!

Max the monster makes mad monster music.

4

Slim the snake slips and slithers everywhere.

Boris Bear bounces on the bed.

Boris bounces on ...

the building blocks and ...

... into the big blue box.

9

I spy toy trouble!

10

Time for toys to tidy up.

All tidy?

Notes for parents and other helpers

Enjoying and talking about the story

CLL 1 listening and responding to stories; **CLL 4** understanding stories

- Remember that the most important thing is to have fun and enjoy the story!

- Make sure that you are both in the mood for a story before you begin.

- Look at the cover and the title. Discuss the 'trouble' that the toys might get into. Show your eagerness to begin reading.

- The pictures are as important as the words: discuss what happens in each. For example, ask **'Where are the children going?'** (page 2) and **'What is happening to the toys?'** (page 3).

- Talk about the toys and their antics – the musical monster, the slithering snake, the bouncing bear.

- On page 7, use your voice to build a sense of anticipation as to where Boris Bear might bounce next.

- Encourage the child to predict events. Ask, **'What will Boris bounce on next?'** (page 7); **'What a mess! I wonder what will happen now?'** (page 9); **'Will the toys get caught?'** (page 11).

- Compare the picture on page 13 with the picture on page 2. Ask, **'Has everything been put back as it was before?'**

Playing with sounds – letter sounds

CLL 3 hear and say initial sounds; **CLL 4** exploring sounds

- Read the story, exaggerating words that begin with the same sound:
  <u>Sl</u>im the <u>s</u>nake <u>sl</u>ips and <u>sl</u>ithers.

- Encourage the child to join in with making sounds shown in the pictures (**'mmmm'**, **'sssss'**, **'boing, boing'**...)

- Point out words beginning with the same sound: for example (pages 2 and 3), **'<u>t</u>ea <u>t</u>ime'** and **'<u>t</u>oy <u>t</u>ime'**. Ask the child if he or she notices other words beginning with the same sound. On page 6, for example, say: **'"Boris" and "Bear" both start with a "b" sound. Did you notice any other words starting with that sound?'**

- On pages 4 to 6 and 9 and 10 you can play 'I-Spy' with the pictures: **'I spy, with my little eye, something beginning with ...** [a particular sound]'. Ask the child to find other items in the picture beginning with the same sound, or point and name a few items and ask the child to spot the two that begin with the same sound.

- Make up more sentences about the toys using words beginning with the same letter: **'<u>Sl</u>im the <u>s</u>nake <u>s</u>ings <u>s</u>illy <u>s</u>ongs'**. Or compose silly sentences about the child's own toys: **'<u>T</u>oby the <u>t</u>iger <u>t</u>ripped over his <u>t</u>ail'**.

- Ensure that these activities are fun. If the child loses interest, stop. Try again another day.

Letters

CLL 3 linking sounds to letters

- Only begin these activities when the child is proficient at identifying sounds and is interested in letters. For example, he or she might point to a letter and ask you what sound it makes.

- Point to the words that begin with the same sound. Point out the letter at the start of the word that makes that sound. Explain, **'That's the letter that makes the "s" sound'**. Ask, **'Can you find another word on the page that begins with the same letter?'**

- Focus on lower-case letters initially. If the child asks about capitals, explain that these are used at the start of names.

- Talk about the shape of the letter, for example (page 5), **'Look – the letter "s" is shaped like a snake!'**

- When looking at pages 4, 5, 6 and 10, ask **'Can you find the letters hidden in the pictures?'**

Book knowledge

CLL 4 knowing about books and print

- Discuss what you are doing as you read. Show the child that you start at the front of the book and turn the pages to see what happens next.

- Use words such as **'cover'**, **'front'**, **'back'**, **'page'**, **'words'** and **'pictures'**.

- Let the child hold the book for you, turn the pages or show you where to start reading.

- Point to the words as you read them. This shows that, in English, print is read from left to right – and that we read the left page before the right.

- Occasionally ask the child to do the pointing for you. If the child seems unwilling, do it yourself: he or she will learn by watching.

First words

CLL 4 reading familiar words

- If the child is showing an interest in the print, explain that you are reading the words. Point to each word as you read it aloud – but still read the text as a story: don't read like a robot!

- If you have read the story before, pause occasionally to encourage the child to 'read' the next word. For example, on page 6: **'"Boris Bear bounces on the b__." What do you think the next word is?'** The picture and letter sound provide a clue; next time the child may read a little more.

- Don't worry if the child says the wrong word, but gets the right meaning. For example (page 8), **'bricks'** rather than **'blocks'** still makes sense and begins with the right sound.

- Draw attention to words that appear on more than one page, such as **'toy'** (pages 3 and 10) and **'the'**. Find the same word on different pages.

- Remember: reading should always be fun – stop if the child loses interest.

Language development

CLL 1 extending vocabulary; using spoken language

- Encourage the child to talk about his or her own toys, or the toys at the nursery.

- Discuss the toys in the story, their characters, what they look like and what they do.

- Talk about where the toys are, using **'on'**, **'in'**, **'under'**, **'by'**. Ask the child, **'Who is on the bed?'** and **'What is under the bed?'**

Retelling the story

CLL 4 retelling narratives; **CLL 2** using language to imagine

- Ask the child to retell the story in his or her own words, turning the pages and using the pictures to help. Don't worry about the actual words on the page.

- Make up your own version of the story using some long-forgotten toys. Imagine what they might do when no-one is looking, using them to act out your story.

Note for schools and nurseries

Each set of activities outlined above relates to the area of learning described as 'Communication, Language and Literacy' (CLL), as set out in the document *Curriculum guidance for the Foundation Stage* (Qualifications and Curriculum Authority, 2000). The aspects of learning covered by **Daisy Lane Home–School Readers** are as follows:

CLL 1 Language for communication   **CLL 3** Linking sounds and letters

CLL 2 Language for thinking   **CLL 4** Reading